BATTLE FOR BRI

BY MONTY STUBBLE

PR

ABOUT THE AUTHOR

Montgomery Stubble (R.A.) served in all the major theatres of the Battle for Britain. He sketched with the Royal Welsh Cartoonists in the opening campaigns before joining the Kings Own Post Modernists, and dropping behind enemy lines to draw with the Free French Impressionists. He was tragically lost in action in the last week of the war, believed to have been hit by a stray pencil sharpener.

On a plain memorial his epitaph reads simply, "I was Monty Stubble."

Published in Great Britain by Private Eye Productions Ltd.
6 Carlisle Street, London W1.,
In association with Andre Deutsch Ltd.,
105-106 Great Russell Street, London WC1
© 1987 Pressdram Ltd.

ISBN 233 98136 5

Printed in Great Britain by
Richard Clay Ltd., Bungay, Suffolk

Written by Ian Hislop and the artist, Nick Newman

CHAPTER ONE

TO HELL AND BACK

IT WAS THE AUGUST AFTER THE CRUSHING DEFEAT OF THE OPPOSITION FORCES, DRIVEN MERCILESSLY BACK BY THE ALL-CONQUERING ARMIES OF THE THIRD RIGHT...

REJOICE! REJOICE!

JAWOHL, HERR THATCHER!

BUT SOMEWHERE BEHIND ENEMY LINES, A SMALL UNIT OF HEROIC MEN WERE LEFT. TIRED AND DEMORALIZED THEY HAD LOST THEIR CAPTAIN, 'TRENCH' FOOT...

CRIPES SARGE! I'VE SHOT CAPTAIN FOOT IN THE BACK!

NO, I DID!

NO, I DID!

WE ALL DID!

THOSE WHO REMAINED WERE AN ASSORTED BUNCH OF BRITS... PLUCKY 'TAFFY' KINNOCK, THE CORPORAL FROM THE WELSH GUARDS, FRESH FROM THE VALLEYS. HE WAS SHORT ON EXPERIENCE, BUT STRONG ON GUTS...

CRIKEY TAFFY-THAT WAS CLOSE!

...PLUCKY 'DARKY' CHATTERJEE OF THE PUNJABI RIFLES, AN OLD CAMPAIGNER FROM THE BACKSTREETS OF BRADFORD...

WELL, TAFFY, LOOKS LIKE ME AND YOU ARE IN CHARGE NOW!

ME AND WHO?

...PLUCKY 'GRANDAD' SHORE FORMERLY OF THE PAY CORPS WAS NOW THRUST INTO ACTION...AND PLUCKY 'FATTY' HEFFER, THE TROUBLEMAKER...

LUMME! WE'RE IN A RIGHT MESS AND MAKE NO MISTAKE!

AND WE ALL KNOW WHOSE FAULT THAT IS!

THIS THEN IS THEIR STORY - THE BATTLE FOR BRITAIN - AND OUR HEROES WERE TO PUT UP A FIGHT THAT WOULD REWRITE THE PAGES OF HISTORY...

OOF!

AARGH!

AFTER HER DECISIVE VICTORY AGAINST THE OPPOSITION, THE FANATICAL HERR THATCHER IS WORRIED BY ANY REMAINING RESISTANCE. IN A BUNKER IN SCHMIDT SQUARE...

ZEY MUST BE ELIMINATED TO REALISE MY DREAM OF A 1,000 YEAR RIGHT!

JA!

JA!

NOT ALL, HOWEVER, WERE JA-MEN. THE IMPETUOUS VON PYM SPOKE UP...

ARE YOU SURE, MEIN FÜHRER, THAT TOTAL WORLD DOMINATION IS A GOOD IDEA?

TAKE VON PYM OUTSIDE AND SHOOT HIM!

JAWOHL!

OBERSTUMMEN GRÜPPENFÜHRER TEBBIT, THE RUTHLESS HATCHET MAN, GLOATED...

ZERE IS NO PROBLEM! ZE OPPOSITION IS WEAK UND SPLINTERED. VE CAN CUT ZEM DOWN AT ANY TIME. HEH! HEH! HEH!

JA! MORE CUTS! CUT EVERYTHING! TEUFEL!

MEANWHILE, NIGHT WAS FALLING ON A MAKESHIFT CAMP. MORALE WAS LOW WHEN 'DARKY' CHATTERJEE BROKE THE SILENCE...

DON'T WORRY, LADS — I'LL TAKE CHARGE!

THAT'S WHAT WE'RE WORRIED ABOUT!

IN TIME OF WAR MEN NEED A STRONG LEADER, AND OUR LADS HAD TO FIND ONE — OR PERISH! 'GRANDAD' SHORE WAS FIRST TO SPEAK...

I'M THE SENIOR ONE HERE!

SENIOR CITIZEN, MORE LIKE!

HA! HA! HA!

'FATTY' HEFFER'S COCKNEY HUMOUR HAD A CRUEL EDGE!

'TAFFY' HAD ANOTHER IDEA...

WHY DON'T WE PUT IT TO THE MEN?

DON'T BE STUPID!

WHAT?!

NOT BLOODY LIKELY!

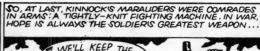

IN HER DOWNINGSTRASSE BUNKER, THE FANATICAL HERR THATCHLER WAS GIVEN UNWELCOME NEWS...

MEIN FÜHRER —ZE POLLS ARE AGAINST YOU!

ZE POLES! KILL ZEM ALL! RAZE ZEM TO ZE GROUND!

NO, YOU MISUNDERSTAND...

VOT? I NEVER MISUNDERSTAND! TAKE HIM OUT AND SHOOT HIM!

COULD THE TIDE OF THE WAR BE TURNING? THE LEADING INDUSTRIALISTS' WHO HAD PUT THATCHLER INTO POWER WERE UNEASY ABOUT THE CONDUCT OF THE WAR...

VE FEEL YOU HAVE MADE A MISTAKE, HERR THATCHLER!

NEIN!

OKAY— NINE MISTAKES!

ELSEWHERE, GENERAL RUDOLF HESSELTINE WAS FLEXING THE MUSCLE OF THE THIRD RIGHT, DESPERATE FOR HIS FIRST TASTE OF ACTION...

ZEY ARE CONSCIENTIOUS OBJECTORS, OBERGRUPPENLIEUTENANT,

ZEN VE MUST BE CONSCIENTIOUS KILLERS, HEH! HEH! HEH!

KRUPPS MISSILE

FEUER!

FEUER!

FEUER!

MEANWHILE, IN A LULL IN THE BATTLE'S DIN, 'DARKY' CHATTERJEE WAS WRITING HIS SENSITIVE WAR POETRY...

"IF I SHOULD DIE, THINK ONLY THIS OF ME..."

GOOD RIDDANCE —THAT'S WHAT I'D THINK!

DO YOU READ ME?

I DON'T READ CHATTERJEE!

FATTY HEFFER'S CRUEL COCKNEY HUMOUR BROKE CHATTERJEE OUT OF HIS REVERIE...

BUT WAR IS A TIME FOR DEEDS, NOT WORDS. TAFFY HAD REORGANIZED HIS DEMORALIZED TROOPS AND PRESENTED HIS FRONT LINE...

I'M NOT GOING TO MAKE THE SAME MISTAKES AS CAPTAIN FOOT. HERE'S OUR NEW BATTLE FORMATION...

"DARKY, GRANDAD, FATTY, HEALEY..."

IT'S THE SAME AS THE OLD ONE!

AS THE SHADOWS FELL, A NERVOUS TAFFY OUTLINED HIS TACTICS...

RIGHT LADS! I'VE GOT MAD MIKE ON THE LEFT...

...AND EVERYONE ELSE ON THE RIGHT!

NEWS BEGAN TO TRICKLE THROUGH OF REVERSES FOR THE ONCE VICTORIOUS THATCHLER — AND TAFFY'S TROUPE TOOK HEART...

WE'RE GOING TO LAUNCH AN OFFENSIVE IN EUROPE!

HANG ON TAFFY, I THOUGHT WE WERE PULLING OUT OF EUROPE?

SHUT UP!

TAFFY WAS HAVING NO TROUBLE IN THE RANKS!

LOOK LADS, NEW LEADER — NEW TACTICS!

NEW LEADER ANYWAY!

IT'LL BE A BOCHE JOB!

FATTY HEFFER'S COCKNEY HUMOUR MADE IT HARD SOMETIMES...

BUT HELP WAS COMING FROM OTHER QUARTERS. IN WAR, EVEN PRIESTS ARE CALLED TO SHOULDER THE BURDEN OF COMBAT. ONE SUCH WAS RESISTANCE HERO, 'RED' KENT...

TAKE THAT, HESSELTINE!

ACH, I AM HIT!

THERE'S A REAL DECORATION, YOU NAZI SWINE!

YOU TELL 'IM 'RED'!

A RED-FACED RUDOLF HESSELTINE JOINED AN URGENT COUNCIL IN THE BUNKER WITH REICHSCHANCELLOR HERMAN LAWSON ADDRESSING A FURIOUS FÜHRER...

VE NEED MORE MONEY, HERR THATCHLER! VE MUST ALL TIGHTEN OUR BELTS!

NEIN!

MEIN GOTT!

TEUFEL!

ONLY THE GROVELLING COMMANDANT LEON BRITISCHER COULD APPEASE THE WRATH OF THE FANATICAL LEADER...

DUMKOPF! ALL YOU BRING IS BAD NEWS! I VANT TO HEAR GOOD NEWS!

I HAVE BUILT 200 MORE P.O.W. CAMPS! STALAGS ARE EVERYWHERE! HEH! HEH!

WUNDERBAR!

GOOD NEWS INDEED!

MEANWHILE WHAT OF THE OTHER COMBATANTS IN THE FIELD? WHAT OF DOC'S PARAMEDICS? THE LEGENDARY 'FLYING DOC' HAD NOT BEEN SEEN FOR MONTHS!

I DON'T LIKE IT... IT'S QUIET!

TOO DAMN QUIET...

THEN WHY DON'T YOU DO SOMETHING?

'BARMY' BENN WAS BACK— AND FIGHTING MAD AS TAFFY'S MARAUDERS SLOWLY APPROACHED THE SMALL WAR TORN TOWN OF CHESTER-LE-FIELD...

I'M GOING TO TAKE IT ON MY OWN!

YOU'RE GOING TO HAVE TO!

CHESTER LE-FIELD

TAFFY INTEVENED...

HANG ON, 'BARMY'— IT'S NOT SAFE!

IT ISN'T?

NOT NOW YOU'RE HERE!

HIMMEL, FRITZ! NOW ZEY ARE SENDING IN ZE CRACKED TROOPS!

FAR AWAY IN THE RIGHT-STAG, OTHERS WERE ALSO WORKING TO OVERTHROW THE THATCHLER REGIME: REBEL GENERALS, LEGENDARY NAMES OF THE FATHERLAND'S GLORIOUS PAST, LIKE VON PYM AND ADMIRAL GROSSER HEATH...

VE VILL HAVE A MASSIVE REVOLT!

WHO?

YOU AND ME!

BUT AT THE LAST MINUTE THEIR ILL-FATED PLOT WAS UNCOVERED BY THE VIGILANT HENCHMEN OF THE THATCHLER BODYGUARD...

TEUFEL! SOMEONE IS PLANTING A BOMB!

THAT'LL BE VON PYM AGAIN. DON'T WORRY, THEY NEVER GO OFF!

ACH! EVERYTHING'S WET!

PARTY CHAIRMAN VON GÜMMER HAD MORE STARTLING NEWS FOR HIS FÜHRER. HE MANAGED TO STAMMER...

ZE THATCHLER YOUTH INFORM ME ZAT ZE PARTY IS BEING INFILTRATED BY NAZIS!

SO VOT?

GUMMKOPF!

HEH! HEH!

BUT THE COST OF WAR IS HIGH IN MEN AND MONEY, AND CHANCELLOR HERMAN LAWSON HAD A DAMAGING REPORT...

ZE ECONOMY IS IN RUINS, ZE MARK IS WORTHLESS!

DON'T BRING MY SON INTO THIS!

IT'S A BAD OMAN!

IN THE PUSH FOR THE KEY TOWN OF CHESTER-LE-FIELD, DOC AND DAVE'S COMMANDOS WERE PINNED DOWN ON THE OUTSKIRTS OF TOWN...

'BARMY'S GOING TO BEAT US TO IT!'

I THOUGHT WE WERE GAINING GROUND!'

WHEN WAS THAT?'

ON THE STREETS, IT WAS DOOR-TO-DOOR FIGHTING, AND 'BARMY' WAS IN FULL CRY...

I'M GOING TO WIN THE WAR! THIS IS THE END OF THATCHLER! HURRAH!'

THAT'S A BIT EXTREME!'

DON'T KNOCK HIM, 'DARKY'!'

VIVE LA LIBÉRATION!'

HISTORY TEACHES THAT IT IS SOMETIMES NECESSARY TO LOSE THE BATTLE IN ORDER TO WIN THE WAR. THE ARMY OF THE RIGHT RETREATED...

VE NEED A MAN LIKE ZAT!'

ON ZE OTHER SIDE! HEH! HEH! HEH!'

ZE FÜHRER WANTS HIM — ALIVE!'

TAFFY KINNOCK WAS WAY BEHIND, SEDUCED FROM ACTION BY THE CHARMS OF POLISH CHANTEUSE MARLENE ULLMAN...

HELLO BIG BOY!'

WE MAKE A GREAT COUPLE!'

...OF COMEDIANS

FATTY HEFFER'S CRUEL COCKNEY HUMOUR SOURED THE MAGIC MOMENT.

BUT TAFFY WAS AS INEXPERIENCED IN LOVE AS HE WAS IN BATTLE...

VOT IS ZE MATTER, TAFFY MY DAHLINK?'

MY GUYS ARE MAD AT ME... ♪

COME 'N FIGHT, TAFFY, YOU WELSH RABBIT!'

BARMY'S MAKING A RIGHT FOOL OF US!'

BUT THE BATTLE FOR CHESTER-LE-FIELD HAD ENDED...

IT'S ALL OVER!'

YOU MEAN BARMY'S BEEN KILLED?'

NO, HE'S WON!'

OH, NO!'

LUMME!'

CRIPES!'

IN WAR THE PENALTY FOR INDECISION IS HIGH, AND TAFFY'S LADS WERE PAYING IT, HOPELESSLY TRAPPED IN THEIR OWN MINES...

LOOK TAFF, THINGS ARE BAD, YOU'VE GOT TO TRUST SAPPER!

SURELY THEY'RE NOT THAT BAD?

WHAT I DON'T KNOW ABOUT MINES ISN'T WORTH... AARGH!

HOWEVER, 'DARKY' CHATTERJEE HAD MISGIVINGS...

...BUT SAPPER'S MAD!

RUBBISH! HE'S AS SANE AS I AM!

OH, NO!

CRIPES!

WE WON'T BE NEEDING THIS!

BULLET BOX

TAFFY WAS IN A TIGHT CORNER AND TRIED TO RALLY THE TROOPS WITH SOME WORDS OF WELSH WISDOM...

REMEMBER LADS! WHEN THE GOING GETS TOUGH...

...THE TAFF GETS GOING!

HA, HA!

HA!

FATTY HEFFER'S CRUEL COCKNEY HUMOUR DEFLATED HIS ROUSING RHETORIC...

ESLEWHERE, DOC HEARD OF TAFFY'S DISASTER ON THE WIRELESS. BUT DECIDED NOT TO HELP...

MAYDAY! MAYDAY!

YOU CAN'T JUST LEAVE HIM, DOC! THAT'S COLLABORATION!

I'VE NEVER COLLABORATED WITH ANYONE!

TRUE!

MEANWHILE IN THE CORRIDORS OF WEISSHALL, THATCHLER'S TRUSTED AIDE, 'MAD' MAX GREGOR, OUTLINED HIS STRATEGY...

I VILL GET RID OF ALL ZE MINES!

MINE GOTT!

YOU DON'T HAVE TO CALL ME ZAT!

BACK IN THE RAVAGED MINEFIELD, THINGS WERE GETTING ROUGH. TAFFY AND DARKY WERE GETTING SCARED...

LOOK SAPPER, WE'RE WORRIED ABOUT CASUALTIES!

LIKE US!

LUMME!

TAFFY IN DIRE STRAITS, HAD DECIDED THAT THERE WAS NOTHING ELSE FOR IT! HE HAD TO LET SAPPER SCARGILL DIRECT HIM...

I'VE GOT NO CHOICE!

NO-ONE EVER HAS WITH SAPPER!

WE'RE ON OUR WAY OUT!

TRUE!

BUT DARKY CHATTERJEE WAS UNSURE AND HUNG BACK.

STOP SLACKING DARKY! WE'RE GOING WITH SAPPER ALL THE WAY! HOORAH!

LOOK BARMY, I GIVE THE ORDERS ROUND HERE!

LIKE WHEN?

FATTY HEFFER'S CRUEL COCKNEY HUMOUR AGAIN LOWERED TAFFY'S MORALE.

BARMY BENN HAD ALREADY MADE HIS MIND UP...

LET'S HAVE A WHIP-ROUND FOR SAPPER! IT'LL CHEER HIM UP!

GOT ANY CHANGE?

I CAN THINK OF ONE!

ELSEWHERE 'MAD' MAX GREGOR, THE FORMER MAN OF STEEL, WAS SHOWING SIGNS OF WEAKNESS – THE ONE THING THE FANATICAL FÜHRER COULD NOT ABIDE...

I LEAVE THE DECISIONS TO YOU– JUST DO VOT I SAY!

JAWOHL MEIN FÜHRER!

YOU MUST STAY FIRM!

YOUR SON'S FIRM?

THE ODIOUS LEON BRITISCHER HAD BAD NEWS FROM ABROAD. THE DESERT WAR HAD TAKEN A BAD TURN, WITH REBEL BEDOUIN CHIEFTAN GADDAFTY LAYING DOWN TERMS...

WE'RE NOT TAKING ORDERS FROM A DICTATOR!

NO MEIN FÜHRER!

QUITE RIGHT!

NEIN!

HIMMEL NO!

VOTEVER YOU SAY!

WAR IS NO GAME FOR AMATEURS. TAFFY WORRIEDLY ADDRESSED THE MEN AND TRIED TO REASSURE THEM...

WE'LL BE ALL RIGHT LADS! WE'VE GOT TIME ON OUR SIDE!

...AND SAPPER!

...AND BARMY!

CRIPES!

OH, NO!

LUMME!

HERR THATCHLER WAS AWAITING THE VISIT OF THE COMMANDER OF THE AFRIKAANS CORPS, VELD-MARSHALL PIETER BOTHA...

...BUT MEIN FÜHRER, HE IS A FASCIST!

WHICH IS WHY I'VE INVITED HIM, GUMKOPF!

BUT A LEADER'S FOLLOWERS MAY NOT BE OF THE SAME CALIBRE — THATCHLER WAS HAVING TROUBLE WITH HER MEN AND ONE WAS CAUGHT IN A BERLIN NIGHTCLUB...

I VILL NOT HAF DEGENERATES IN ZE PARTY.

VOT ABOUT VON PORKINSON?

SHUT UP!

BACK IN THE MINEFIELD, THE TRAPPED MARAUDERS WERE FORCED TO CONSIDER A TRUCE...

IT'S NOT SURRENDER, SAPPER. JUST TALKS...

...ABOUT SURRENDERING.

FATTY HEFFER'S CRUEL COCKNEY HUMOUR RANG TRUE.

BUT SAPPER WAS DETERMINED TO FIGHT TO THE DEATH.

WE CAN'T GIVE UP NOW!

WELL, CAN WE GIVE UP LATER?

WHILE TAFFY WAS STUCK IN THE MINES, TIME WAS TICKING AWAY BEFORE THE BIG OFFENSIVE IN EUROPE...

LOOK, BOYOS! WE'VE GOT TO HAVE A CLEAR PLAN. WE'LL STAY IN EUROPE, THEN WITHDRAW MAYBE, OR MAYBE NOT OR SOME- THING...

LUMME!

CRIPES!

CAPTAIN FOOT'S DIARY

ALL THE COMBATANTS WERE KEYED UP TO FEVER PITCH ON THE FATEFUL EVE OF THE BATTLE FOR EUROPE...

Z Z Z

A SHOCK RAN THROUGH THE LADS WHEN SAPPER WAS CAPTURED BY THE ENEMY WHILST ON PATROL ...

BUT SAPPER REFUSED TO TALK: 'MAD' MAX GREGOR HAD MET HIS MATCH ...

'MAD' MAX WAS REMOVED FROM THE FRONT LINE BY THE CRAZED FÜHRER, WHO WAS FURTHER ENRAGED AT THE LEAKING OF HER SECRET PLANS TO THE ENEMY ...

MEANWHILE SAPPER ESCAPED. THERE WAS GREAT JUBILATION IN TAFFY'S GANG ...

AS WAR CLOUDS GATHERED, THE LEGENDARY DOC OWEN AND PLUCKY 'JOCK' STEEL PLANNED THEIR ALLIED ASSAULT. THIS TIME, THE GLORY WOULD BE THEIRS ...

TAFFY'S LADS WERE FIRMLY COMMITTED TO TAKE EUROPE, BUT TAFFY WAS AFTER A FRESH APPROACH ...

FATTY HEFFER'S CRUEL COCKNEY HUMOUR LOWERED MORALE YET AGAIN. ONLY THE BATTLE WOULD TELL ...

TAFFY KINNOCK WAS GETTING COCKY ABOUT THE MARAUDERS' RECENT SUCCESSES AGAINST THE RIGHT...

SOMEONE NOT LAUGHING IN THE BACKGROUND WAS GRUFF VETERAN SERGEANT 'BUTCHER' HEALEY, WHO HAD BEEN PASSED OVER MORE THAN ONCE...

FATTY HEFFER'S CRUEL COCKNEY HUMOUR MOCKED THE OLD-TIMER.

BUT 'BUTCHER' HAD A REPUTATION FOR A CLEVER REPLY HIMSELF, AND ELOQUENTLY PUT HEFFER DOWN...

'MAD' MAX GREGOR WAS STILL TRYING TO DRAW UP A TRUCE WITH 'SAPPER' AND THE LADS BUT THE FÜHRER WAS GROWING IMPATIENT...

AFTER THE LOSSES IN EUROPE DOC 'KILLER OWEN AND WEE JOCK STEEL WERE LICKING THEIR WOUNDS, BUT AT LAST DOC HAD SOME GOOD NEWS...

MEANWHILE IN THE HAZY SUMMER SKIES, THE BATTLE OVER LONDON WAS GOING AGAINST THE FÜHRER. SPITFIRE ACE 'RED' KEN SHOT DOWN LUFTWAFFLE COMMANDER PATROECH JUNKERS, AS HE TRIED TO CARRY OUT THATCHLER'S PLAN TO WIPE LONDON OFF THE FACE OF THE EARTH...

UP ALOFT AMIDST THE WISPY CLOUDS IN THE STILL BLUE SKY, SPITFIRE ACE 'RED' KEN AND HIS GLORY BOYS WERE STILL ENGAGED IN DOG-FIGHTS WITH PATROECH 'BOMBER' JUNKERS OVER THE BLITZED CITIES OF ENGLAND...

SUDDENLY OUT OF THE SUN CAME LEFT WING COMMANDER 'RED' KEN, GUNS BLAZING...BUT THE DUEL IN THE SKY WAS INCONCLUSIVE...

BACK ON THE GROUND, 'SAPPER' WAS LOOKING FOR SOME GLORY OF HIS OWN...

BUT SOME OF THE LADS FROM 'SAPPER'S' CORPS OF SABOTEURS HAD INFILTRATED THE PORTS AND WERE PLAYING MERRY HELL...

AS IF THIS WAS NOT ENOUGH, THE BELEAGUERED HERR THATCHLER LEARNT OF A FRESH DISASTER IN HER SECURITY FORCES, LORD HOWE-HOWE BROKE THE NEWS...

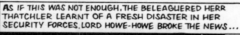

IT WAS THE FÜHRER'S DARKEST HOUR :- THE BLITZ WAS FAILING, 'MAD' MAX GREGOR WAS LOSING, THE WAR ECONOMY WAS IN RUINS, AND HER HENCHMEN WERE GETTING RESTLESS...

CHAPTER TWO

CODENAME: VALOUR

IN WAR, A COMMANDER HAS TO LEAD FROM THE FRONT. TAFFY HAD YET TO LEARN THE FIRST LAW OF COMBAT...

THIS WAY TAFF!

RIGHT SAPPER!

IT'S A DOG'S LIFE, EH, TAFF?

HA HA HA!

FATTY HEFFER'S CRUEL COCKNEY HUMOUR WAS TOO CLOSE FOR COMFORT.

BUT A WORRIED 'GRANDAD' SHORE SPOKE UP FOR THE OLD GUARD IN THE MARAUDERS...

SHUT UP FATTY! WE'RE A SELECT BAND OF FIGHTING MEN!

AND I'LL DO THE SELECTING!

NOT WHILE I'M IN CHARGE!

WHEN'S THAT?

FINALLY TAFFY HAD TO ASSERT HIMSELF. HE NEEDED A BIG PUSH AS THERE WOULD BE NO OFFENSIVE UNTIL THE AUTUMN...

THIS IS IT! I'VE GOT HER ON THE RUN! AARGH!

STRETCHER!

HE DIDN'T EVEN WORRY 'ER!

THE RED CRASS

CRIPES!

MEANWHILE IN THE SULTRY SUMMER SKIES, SPITFIRE ACE RED' KEN AND HIS FLYBOYS WERE TAUNTING THE LUFTWAFFLE COMMANDER PATROECH 'BOMBER' JUNKERS.

COME 'N GET ME, SQUAREHEAD!

TEUFEL! HE'S ON A SUICIDE MISSION!

NEIN, YOU ARE!

BACK IN DOWNING STRASSE BEFORE GOING ON HOLIDAY TO A SWISS HIDEAWAY, THE FÜHRER WAS CONDUCTING A FINAL BRIEFING...

VE MUST GET ZE DEBTS FROM EUROPE!

HOW?

HE WON'T BE ANY USE!

FRUSTRATED AT THE STALEMATE IN THE MINEFIELD SAPPER WAS BEGINNING TO FIGHT DIRTY...

MY LADS AND I ARE FIGHTING FOR THE FUNDAMENTAL RIGHT OF EVERY MAN IN THIS COUNTRY TO...

ACHTUNG! GAS!

A MYSTERIOUS EAST EUROPEAN GO-BETWEEN APPEARED FROM THE SHADOWS TO ARRANGE A TRUCE BETWEEN SAPPER'S BELEAGUERED CREW AND 'MAD MAX' GREGOR...

WHY HAVEN'T THEY COME? I COULD END IT ALL!

THAT'S WHY THEY HAVEN'T COME!

CZECH POINT

AS OFTEN IN WAR, IT ALL FELL THROUGH.

HEADING FOR LONDON, WITH THE SUN GLINTING ON HIS WINGS, WAS SPITFIRE ACE 'RED' KEN AND HIS DEATH-OR-GLORY DAREDEVIL FLY-BOYS. BUT THE FÜHRER HAD GROUNDED THE LUFTWAFFLE AND THE SKIES WERE EMPTY.

THE COWARDS WON'T COME AND FIGHT!

THEY'RE YELLOW, 'RED'!

SCRAMBLE!

IT WILL BE!

RAF SOUTHBANK

ELSEWHERE, AT A SECRET RENDEZVOUS, A RATTLED 'MADMAX' GREGOR FINALLY FACED SAPPER...

YOU CAN'T HIDE BEHIND A BAG!

LEAVE HERR THATCHLER OUT OF THIS!

MEANWHILE THE WEARY ALLIES HAD PITCHED CAMP, AND WERE BEING ENTERTAINED BY A CONCERT PARTY FROM ENSPPA. STARRING THE DARLING OF THE FORCES, THE GIRL THEY'D LEFT BEHIND...

IT AIN'T HALF BAD, MUM

PACK UP YER TROUBLES IN YER OLD KIT BAG...

WHAT A DRAG!

IT ISN'T BIG ENOUGH!

NO, IT'S SHIRL!

THE SHOW CONTINUED WITH SOME MUSIC-HALL TURNS TO KEEP THE TROOPS SMILING...

I SAY, I SAY, I SAY...

I'M THE ONLY ONE WHO SAYS ANYTHING ROUND HERE!

WHO'S THE OLD COMEDIAN?

IT'S WOY!

WHO'S NEXT ON THE BILL?

BILL WHO?

IN THE DEPTHS OF DOWNING STRASSE, HERR THATCHLER WAS PURGING HER CLOSEST ADVISERS, REPLACING REBELS WITH HER FANATICALLY LOYAL BROWNNOSES...

PRIOR, I'M REPLACING YOU WITH A TURD!

HURD, MEIN FÜHRER!

I KNOW VOT I'M SAYING GUMBAG SCHWEIN!

AT THE LADS' BIG COUNCIL OF WAR, TAFFY HAD BEEN WORRIED BY 'SAPPER'S' ACTIVITIES...

I DON'T LIKE VIOLENCE, 'SAPPER'!

THEN YOU'D BETTER AGREE WITH ME!

CRIPES!

BUT 'SAPPER' HAD GONE TOO FAR EVEN FOR THE HARSH NECESSITIES OF WAR, AND WAS CALLED BEFORE A COURT-MARTIAL...

WE'LL HAVE TO SENTENCE HIM IN HIS ABSENCE...

FINE!

ISN'T THAT A BIT STIFF?

BACK IN THE MINEFIELD, 'SAPPER' RECEIVED HELP FROM AN UNEXPECTED QUARTER, FROM FATHER JENKINS, THE BATTLING PADRE...

GOD BLESS YOU, SAPPER!

GOD IS ON OUR SIDE!

YES I AM!

HARD ON HIS HEELS CAME REINFORCEMENTS — MORE BATTLING PADRES FRESH FROM YEARS BEHIND THE LINES. THEY WERE LED BY THE LEGENDARY ARCHIE 'KILLER' RUNCIE...

♩...ONWARD CHRISTIAN SOLDIERS...♩

OH NO!

IT'S THE CHURCH MILITANT!

I LIKE IT!

MEANWHILE AT THE ANNUAL NUREMBERG RALLY, RIGHT-CHANCELLOR HELMUT LAWSON OUTLINED HIS BOLD NEW STRATEGY FOR THE WAR ECONOMY...

DÖLE NEIN COAL

VE HAF NO CAUSE FOR COMPLACENCY... EVERYTHING IS JUST FINE...

HE'S USELESS VE SHOULD GET VON PORKINSON ON ZE JOB!

NOT AGAIN!

HEH, HEH, HEH!

VON PYM'S CRUEL REBEL HUMOUR MOCKED THE FÜHRER'S FALLEN FAVOURITE...

BUT NOTHING DAUNTED THE FANATICAL HERR THATCHLER, AS SHE WHIPPED UP THE PARTY FAITHFUL ON THE LONG, DRAWN-OUT BATTLE FOR THE MINEFIELDS...

MY DREAM IS REALIZED... ZE 1000 YEAR STRIKE!

COA

SIEG HEIL SIEG HEIL SIEG HEIL

THE POWER-CRAZED LEADER OF THE THIRD RIGHT HAD HAD ENOUGH OF HER ELDERLY MINE COMMANDANT 'MAD' MAX GREGOR...

WITH 'MAD' MAX WITHDRAWN FROM THE FRONT, THE SOFT-TALKING VOICE OF REPLACEMENT 'OBERRATED LIEUTENANT OESTEN FLOATED OVER FROM ENEMY LINES...

THE YOUNG WELSH CORPORAL FROM THE VALLEYS WAS STILL TRYING TO GIVE HIS COMRADES THE LEADERSHIP THAT WOULD ONE DAY OVERTURN THE EVIL FÜHRER—BUT BARMY WAS IN A MILITANT MOOD!

THE FANATICAL HERR THATCHLER TURNED A MORE HUMAN FACE TO HER PEOPLE AS SHE TRIED TO KEEP THEIR SUPPORT FOR THE WAR EFFORT...

BUT IN WAR AN ARMY NEEDS THE DRIVE OF AN EFFICIENT ECONOMY BEHIND THE TROOPS, AND THE RIGHT WAS FALTERING...

IN WEISSHALL, THATCHLER'S LIEUTENANTS SPELT OUT THE MESSAGE...

After Taffy Kinnock had redrawn his lines of command, with Corporal 'Jerry' Kaufman and gruff Sergeant 'Butcher' Healey in the forefront, Sapper dropped a new BOMBSHELL.

Meanwhile, the soft-spoken voice of Mad Max's Lieutenant drifted across no-man's land...

'Mad' Max Gregor, striving to keep in favour with an impatient and unbalanced Führer, gave a progress report on his new tactics...

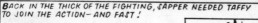
Back in the thick of the fighting, Sapper needed Taffy to join the action — and fast!

In a secret chamber somewhere in Vest Münster, the sinister industrialists behind the rise of the Führer's régime were having doubts...

And so she announced her programme for the forthcoming year to her sycophantic henchmen...

DEEP IN VESTMÜNSTER, FAILED GENERAL 'MAD' MAX GREGOR WAS ON THE CARPET AGAIN ...

MEANWHILE SAPPER, DEFYING A COURT MARTIAL FOR WAR CRIMES, WAS FIGHTING ON IN THE MINEFIELD, CALLING FOR 'BIG' NORM WILLIS TO HELP ...

FATTY HEFFER'S CRUEL COCKNEY HUMOUR SAVAGED THE BLUFF SOLDIER'S HESITATION ...

HIGH IN THE SKY ABOVE, SPITFIRE ACE 'RED' KEN DREAMED HIS DREAMS OF VICTORY, DEFYING THE MIGHT OF THE LUFTWAFFLE ...

BACK IN VESTMÜNSTER THE UNBALANCED LEADER OF THE RIGHT WAS CONFRONTED BY A DELEGATION OF REBEL OFFICERS LED BY BITTER ADMIRAL GROSSER HEATH ...

THE FÜHRER WAS CRUMBLING UNDER THE PRESSURE, AS HER SINISTER MINISTER FOR RE-EDUCATION FRANZ JOSEPH ADMITTED HE HAD MISCALCULATED IN TRYING TO RAISE MONEY FROM THATCHLER'S LOYAL SUPPORTERS ...

EVEN IN WAR THE SPIRIT OF CHRISTMAS IS NOT TOTALLY LOST. ABOVE THE SOUND OF SINGING IN NO-MAN'S LAND CAME A STILL SMALL VOICE ...

A CRESTFALLEN SAPPER WAS TRYING TO ORGANISE A WHIP-ROUND FROM HIS LADS FOR THEIR COMRADES WOUNDED IN THE STRUGGLE FOR THE MINEFIELD...

SORRY SAPPER!

TERRIBLY SORRY SAPPER!

DIG DEEP

IT'S ONLY TEN BOB! COME ON, FORK OUT!

FORK OFF!

MEANWHILE BACK AT RAF SOUTHBANK, SPITFIRE ACE 'RED' KEN WAS BEING COLD-SHOULDERED BY HIS FLYBOYS FOR TURNING TAIL IN THE BATTLE FOR LONDON...

KEN'S BEEN SENT TO COVENTRY!

IT'S NOT FAR ENOUGH!

NO BOTTLE PLACE

HEY CHAPS! IS THIS THE MESS?

IT CERTAINLY IS!

BUT WAR IS FULL OF SURPRISES, AND SUDDENLY KINNOCK'S MARAUDERS FOUND THEMSELVES GAINING GROUND AND ADVANCING ON THE FORCES OF THE RIGHT...

HANG ON TAFF! SOMETHING'S WRONG!

WE'RE GOING FORWARD!

THAT'S IT!

FATTY HEFFER'S CRUEL COCKNEY HUMOUR WAS UNGENEROUS IN TAFFY'S HOUR OF GLORY...

ELSEWHERE, AT A MASS RALLY AT LUFFENBURG, THE THATCHLER YOUTH WERE RUNNING RIOT...

NFCS

TEUFEL! ZEY ARE DESTROYING EVERYTHING!

ZEY LEARN FAST, HEIN?

GUMBAG SCHWEIN!

THE FANATICAL FÜHRER, HOWEVER WAS AWAY—DESPERATELY SEEKING ALLIANCES IN THE FAR EAST WITH THE SLANT-EYED PERIL. SHE TRIED TO QUELL UNEASE ABOUT HER CONDUCT OF THE WAR...

I ASSURE YOU, ZERE ARE NO PROBLEMS IN ZE FATHERLAND TODAY!

JA - SHE FLYS HOME TOMORROW!

BANZAI!

HURRO THATCHRER!

BUT THE WAR-WEARY FÜHRER OFFENDED HER INSCRUTABLE HOSTS WITH A MAJOR DIPLOMATIC GAFFE...

I HAF GREAT RESPECT FOR YOUR STRONG GOVERNMENT HERE IN... ER... CHILE?

OH NO!

MEIN GOTT!

IT LOOK LIKE SHE LOST!

SO! I THOUGHT SHE SAID SHE WON.

IN THE HAZY BLUE SUMMER SKIES ABOVE LONDON, SPITFIRE ACE 'RED' KEN WAS PREPARING TO TRANSFER, TO SUPPORT TAFFY KINNOCK.

SORRY LADS I'M OFF!

DON'T DESERT US NOW, 'RED', LONDON NEEDS YOU!

BUT I DON'T NEED LONDON!

BLIMEY!

BACK IN THE MESS, 'RED' GOT AN EARFUL FROM THE FLYBOYS AT RAF SOUTHBANK...

YOU'RE JUST A GLORY HUNTER 'RED'!

DON'T GO 'RED', THERE'S ONLY A FEW OF US LEFT!

AND THAT DOESN'T INCLUDE HIM!

BLOOMING HECK!

CRIPES!

MEANWHILE HERMAN FOWLER OF THE SINISTER WAFFEN DHSS WAS PLANNING A SWEEPING NEW CAMPAIGN AGAINST THE CIVILIAN POPULATION...

IT'S FOR THEIR OWN BENEFIT!

YE'RE NOT GIVING ZEM ANY!

HEH! HEH!

SERPS

THE CORPULENT RIGHT CHANCELLOR IN HIS WESTMÜNSTER EYRIE WAS STILL GRAPPLING WITH THE INSOLUBLE PROBLEMS OF THE WAR ECONOMY...

MEIN FÜHRER, VE ARE GROSSLY INFLATED!

SPEAK FOR YOURSELF, FAT SCHWEIN!

OH, NO! THATCHLER'S EXPLODED!

IT'S THE ONLY BOOM WE'RE GOING TO SEE ROUND HERE!

ON THE GROUND, KINNOCK'S MARAUDERS WERE ASSESSING FOWLER'S FEARSOME NEW OFFENSIVE...

THEY'VE GOT NO MERCY! THEY'RE ATTACKING THE WEAK AND DEFENCESS!

HERE THEY COME!

CRIKEY!

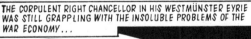

FATTY HEFFER'S CRUEL COCKNEY HUMOUR MADE SHORT SHRIFT OF TAFFY'S WELSH RHETORIC.

THE EVIL HENCHMEN SURROUNDING THE MAD FÜHRER WERE INCREASINGLY WORRIED ABOUT HER PLANS FOR THEM...

YOU CAN'T RESHUFFLE US, MEIN FÜHRER!

VE ARE NOT A PACK OF CARDS!

NEIN! YOU ARE A PACK OF IDIOTS! SHOOT EVERYONE!

CHAPTER THREE

TUNES OF GLORY

IT WAS CHRISTMAS, AND THE EVIL GENERAL VON TEBBIT WAS BEGINNING TO WAGE A PERSONAL CAMPAIGN AGAINST HIS DEADLY ADVERSARY— TAFFY KINNOCK OF THE COMMANDOS...

YOU'RE A FASCIST THUG, VON TEBBIT!

THANKS! I COULD EAT YOU FOR BREAKFAST!

WELL, YOU HAVEN'T BEATEN ME YET!

YOU LOOK PRETTY SMASHED TO ME! HEH! HEH!

LAWKS-A-MERCY!

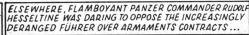

ELSEWHERE, FLAMBOYANT PANZER COMMANDER RUDOLF HESSELTINE WAS DARING TO OPPOSE THE INCREASINGLY DERANGED FÜHRER OVER ARMAMENTS CONTRACTS...

MEIN FÜHRER, ZE FATHERLAND DESPERATELY NEEDS ZE CHOPPER!

DON'T TALK TO ME ABOUT VON PORKINSON!

YEST-LAND

IT'S A BIG ASSET!

DON'T BE DISGUSTING, HESSELSCHWEIN!

THE SINISTER LEADER OF THE WAFFEN DHSS HERMAN FOWLER WAS PLAYING HIS PART IN THE FESTIVE MOOD...

CHRISTMAS IS A TIME FOR GIVING TO ZE POOR AND NEEDY...

ZAT'S ZE SPIRIT!

...SO I'M GIVING ZEM A NASTY SHOCK!

I'M DREAMING OF A WHITE PAPER!

EVEN IN DOWNINGSTRASSE, THE FÜHRER PERMITTED A SMALL CELEBRATION AMONGST HER EVIL HENCHMEN...

I'VE DECLARED A CEASE-FIRE. I WON'T FIRE ANYONE TILL AFTER CHRISTMAS!

WUNDERBAR, MEIN YULETIDE FÜHRER!

BRING OUT ZE CHRISTMAS DECORATIONS!

I'LL HAVE A KNIGHTHOOD!

ACROSS THE WINTRY WASTES OF NO-MAN'S-LAND CAME THE FAINT SOUND OF SINGING FROM THE ALLIED LINES...

ONCE IN ROYAL DAVID'S CITY...

DON'T GET CARRIED AWAY DOC!

I WISH HE WOULD BE!

AND AMONGST KINNOCK'S MARAUDERS THE HELL OF WAR WAS SUSPENDED AS THE BATTLE-WEARY COMMANDOS RELAXED IN CHRISTMAS CHEER...

TAFFY'S GOT A FUNNY HAT ON!

WHAT'S FUNNY ABOUT HATTON?

LET'S FORGET THE WAR AND PLAY CHARADES!

I THOUGHT YOU SAID FORGET THE WAR!

FATTY HEFFER'S CRUEL COCKNEY HUMOUR MADE NO ALLOWANCE FOR SEASONAL GOODWILL.

CHAPTER FOUR

NO SURRENDER